This
Treasure Cove Story
belongs to

_____

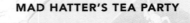

MAD HATTER'S TEA PARTY

A CENTUM BOOK 978-1-912396-66-5
Published in Great Britain by Centum Books Ltd.
This edition published 2018.

3 5 7 9 10 8 6 4 2

Centum Books Ltd, 20 Devon Square, Newton Abbot, Devon, TQ12 2HR, UK.
9/10 Fenian St, Dublin 2, D02 RX24, Ireland.

www.centumbooksltd.co.uk | books@centumbooksltd.co.uk
CENTUM BOOKS Limited Reg.No. 07641486.

A CIP catalogue record for this book is available
from the British Library.

Printed in China.

A Treasure Cove Story

Disney

ALICE
in
WONDERLAND

Mad Hatter's Tea Party

Pictures by Walt Disney Studios.

Retold by Jane Werner. Adapted by Richmond I Kelsey and
Don Griffith from the motion picture based on the story by Lewis Carroll.

THERE WAS ONCE a Mad Hatter, a peculiar
fellow, who lived in a strange little house in the woods
of Wonderland.

Nearby lived a friend of his, the March Hare.

One day the March Hare heard (through the wild grapevine of course) that it was the Mad Hatter's birthday.

So he baked and iced a birthday cake. Then down the
woodland path he went, singing as he skipped along:

The very merriest birthday to you!
The very merriest birthday to you!

The Mad Hatter was delighted. He called his friend
the Dormouse, a sleepy little soul, and what a jolly

time they all did have! They decided a birthday party
was the best of all possible fun.

The next day, the Mad Hatter kept thinking of that party and of all the jolly songs they sang. He did wish they could have another party.

The March Hare was thinking about it too. How he longed for another piece of birthday cake!

And the sleepy Dormouse wished for another cup of tea.

But it was nobody's birthday that day.

The Mad Hatter had just had his. The March Hare's was months and months away. And the Dormouse had been so sleepy when his mother told him about his birthday, that he couldn't remember it at all.

'Oh me!' sighed the March Hare. 'Nothing but un-birthdays as far as I can see. It really isn't fair. Only one birthday a year and 364 un-birthdays!'

'364 un-birthdays!' cried the Mad Hatter. 'Well, fine. Splendid! Let's celebrate those!'

So they did. Every day they had an un-birthday party. Every day they set up the table, hung up the decorations and had birthday cake and tea.

And after the party they cleared everything away. But that soon got tiresome. So they set up a great long table underneath the trees. They put chairs all around, and cups and plates, and pots and pots of tea.

After that they never cleared away. When things got messy, the Mad Hatter would call out, 'Move down! Move down!'

And the March Hare would call out, 'Clean cups! Clean cups!' And away they would move, to new places at the table.

So the un-birthday party went on and on. And every day they happily sang…

A very merry un-birthday to you!
A very merry un-birthday to you!

All that singing and moving around got to be too
much for the sleepy Dormouse. Since he was so fond of
tea, he just chose himself a teapot, climbed in and stayed
there. Now and then he would open a drowsy eye and
join in a bit of the fun.

As Alice walked through the Wonderland Woods, seeing the most unusual sights, she heard the singing through the trees. *It sounds like a birthday party* she thought, so she hurried along to see.

In through the Mad Hatter's gate she stepped. She saw the coloured lanterns hanging from the trees and cakes on the table. And she heard the jolly song...

A very merry un-birthday to you! To who?
A very merry un-birthday to me!
Then the Mad Hatter saw her.
'No room!' he cried. 'What are you doing here?'

'Why, there seems to be lots of room,' Alice said. 'I heard you singing in the woods and it sounded so delightful –'

'It did?' cried the Mad Hatter. 'What a charming child. Come in, my dear. Sit down, sit down.'

They urged her into an empty chair.

'Whose birthday is it?' Alice asked.

'No one's. It's an un-birthday party,' they said and explained what an un-birthday party was.

'Why, then it's my un-birthday, too!' Alice said.

A very merry un-birthday to you!

A very merry un-birthday to you!

chorused the Mad Hatter and the March Hare.

'Why don't you have some tea?' they asked.

'Yes, thank you,' Alice said. 'Just half a cup please.'

The Mad Hatter snatched up a carving knife and he cut a cup in two.

'My,' said Alice, 'I wish Dinah were here to see this.'

'And who is Dinah?' the March Hare asked.

'Dinah is my cat,' Alice said.

'Cat! Cat! Cat!' cried a horrified voice. And the
Dormouse, at the sound of that dreaded word, popped
out of his teapot, up into the air.

'Well, I never thought –' Alice began, as the
Dormouse floated slowly down, singing to himself.

'Would you like some more tea?' asked the Mad Hatter.

'How can I have more?' asked Alice, 'when I haven't had any yet?'

'Oh, well, all right, don't,' sulked the Mad Hatter and he drank the tea himself.

'Move down! Move down!' cried the March Hare, then, 'Clean cups! Clean cups!'

'Move down!' scolded the Mad Hatter, pushing Alice out of her chair.

'This is the silliest party I've ever seen,' said Alice. 'I'd rather have one birthday party a year and know what I'm about.'

She stalked out of the gate and off through the woods. No one seemed to notice that she had left. She could hear them singing behind her…

A very merry un-birthday to us!

There they are singing, to this very day, drinking cups of un-birthday tea. If you should wander through Wonderland, the Wonderland of dreams, perhaps you will find a little house in the woods and hear voices singing loud and free…

A very merry un-birthday to you! To who?
A very merry un-birthday to me!

Treasure Cove Stories

Please contact Centum Books to receive the full list of titles in the *Treasure Cove Stories* series.
books@centumbooksltd.co.uk

Classic favourites

1 Three Little Pigs
2 Snow White and the Seven Dwarfs
3 The Fox and the Hound
- Hide-and-Seek
4 Dumbo
5 Cinderella
6 Cinderella's Friends
7 Alice in Wonderland
8 Mad Hatter's Tea Party from Alice in Wonderland
9 Mickey Mouse and his Spaceship
10 Peter Pan
11 Pinocchio
12 Mickey and the Beanstalk
13 Sleeping Beauty and the Good Fairies
14 The Lucky Puppy
15 Chicken Little
16 The Incredibles
17 Coco
18 Winnie the Pooh and Tigger
19 The Sword in the Stone
20 Mary Poppins
21 The Jungle Book
22 The Aristocats
23 Lady and the Tramp
24 Bambi
25 Bambi - Friends of the Forest

Recently published

50 Frozen
51 Cinderella is my Babysitter
52 Beauty and the Beast
- I am the Beast
53 Blaze and the Monster Machines
- Mighty Monster Machines
54 Blaze and the Monster Machines
- Dino Parade!
55 Teenage Mutant Ninja Turtles
- Follow the Ninja!

56 I am a Princess
57 The Big Book of Paw Patrol
58 Paw Patrol
- Adventures with Grandpa!
59 Paw Patrol - Pirate Pups!
60 Trolls
61 Trolls Holiday
62 The Secret Life of Pets
63 Zootropolis
64 Ariel is my Babysitter
65 Tiana is my Babysitter
66 Belle is my Babysitter
67 Paw Patrol
- Itty-Bitty Kitty Rescue
68 Moana
69 Nella the Princess Knight
- My Heart is Bright!
70 Guardians of the Galaxy
71 Captain America
- High-Stakes Heist!
72 Ant-Man
73 The Mighty Avengers
74 The Mighty Avengers
- Lights Out!
75 The Incredible Hulk
76 Shimmer & Shine
- Wish Upon a Sleepover
77 Shimmer & Shine - Backyard Ballet
78 Paw Patrol - All-Star Pups!
79 Teenage Mutant Ninja Turtles
- Really Spaced Out!
80 I am Ariel
81 Madagascar
82 Jasmine is my Babysitter
83 How to Train your Dragon
84 Shrek
85 Puss in Boots
86 Kung Fu Panda
87 Beauty and the Beast - I am Belle
88 The Lion Guard
- The Imaginary Okapi
89 Thor - Thunder Strike!
90 Guardians of the Galaxy
- Rocket to the Rescue!
91 Nella the Princess Knight
- Nella and the Dragon
92 Shimmer & Shine
- Treasure Twins!

93 Olaf's Frozen Adventure
94 Black Panther
95 Trolls
- Branch's Bunker Birthday
96 Trolls - Poppy's Party
97 The Ugly Duckling
98 Cars - Look Out for Mater!
99 101 Dalmatians
100 The Sorcerer's Apprentice
101 Tangled
102 Avengers
- The Threat of Thanos
103 Puppy Dog Pals
- Don't Rain on my Pug-Rade
104 Jurassic Park
105 The Mighty Thor
106 Doctor Strange

Latest publications

107 Captain Marvel
108 The Invincible Iron Man
109 Black Panther
- Warriors of Wakanda
110 The Big Freeze
111 Ratatouille
112 Aladdin
113 Aladdin - I am the Genie
114 Seven Dwarfs Find a House
115 Toy Story
116 Toy Story 4
117 Paw Patrol - Jurassic Bark!
118 Paw Patrol
- Mighty Pup Power!
119 Shimmer & Shine
- Pet Talent Show!
120 SpongeBob SquarePants
- Krabby Patty Caper
121 The Lion King - I am Simba
122 Winnie the Pooh
- The Honey Tree
123 Frozen II
124 Baby Shark and the Colours of the Ocean
125 Baby Shark and the Police Sharks!
126 Trolls World Tour

Book list may be subject to change.